M000087877

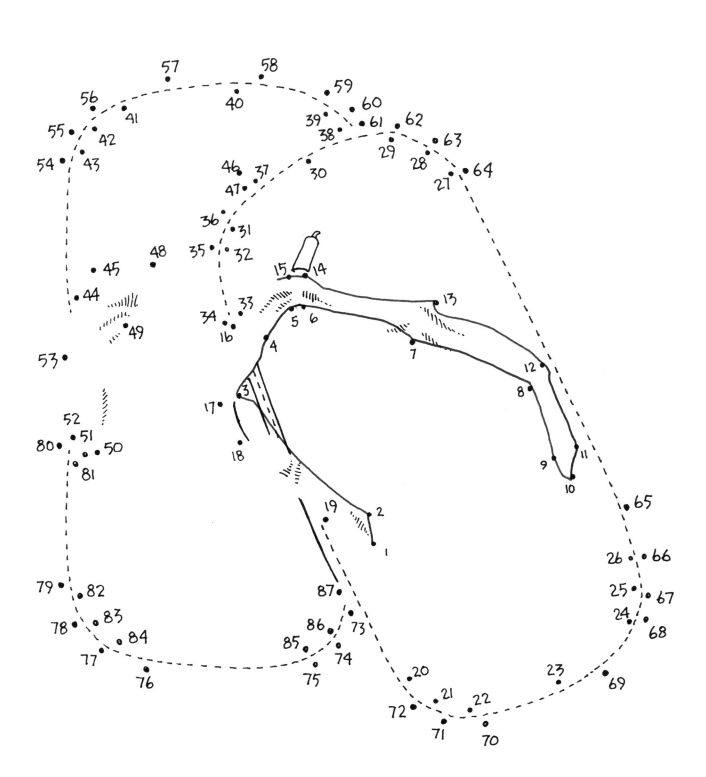

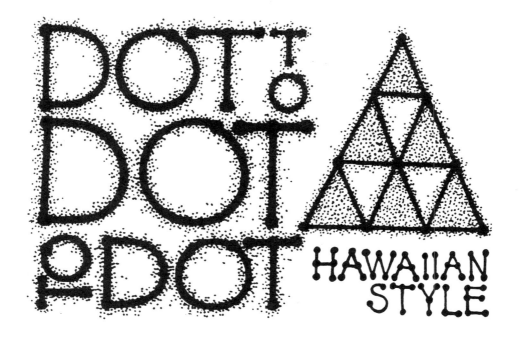

DOT TO DOT TO DOT TO DOT A

HAWAIIAN STYLE

BY

WREN.

for all the children of Hawaii
especially for my own keiki
···elijah gabriel···

MnM Books

TABLE OF CONTENTS

1· slippers
2· petroglyph
3· fern ··· lauaʻe
4· gourd drum ··· ipu
5· snail ··· kama loli
6· laulau
7· pig ··· puaʻa
8· ukulele
9· mynah ··· piha ʻekelo
10· bird of paradise ··· pua
11· banana ··· maiʻa
12· shave ice
13· anthurium ··· pua
14· dolphin ··· naiʻa
15· nēnē goose
16· gourd helmet ··· mākini
17· gourd rattle ··· uli uli
18· hibiscus ··· aloalo
19· humuhumunukunukuapuaʻa
20· turtle ··· honu
21· taro ··· kalo
22· shell ··· pūpū
23· octopus ··· heʻe
24· pineapple ··· hala kahiki
25· gecko ··· moʻo
26· breadfruit quilt ··· ʻulu
27· maile lei
28· hula dancer
29· whale ··· koholā
30· orchid ··· pua

when you finish connecting the dots,
add some of your own lines and
colors to make it especially yours.

3.

34 42
43
33 44
45
30 31 46
29 32 47
41
28 49
48 50
27
25 52 51
24 26 54
53 55
23 56
22 57
35 60 61
21 58
20 59
19
40 62
18 63
17 66
64
14 16 67
13 65
15
68
12
69 72 73
11 71
8 10 36 70
9 74
7 39 75
6
5 76
4
77
3
2
1 78

37 38

4.

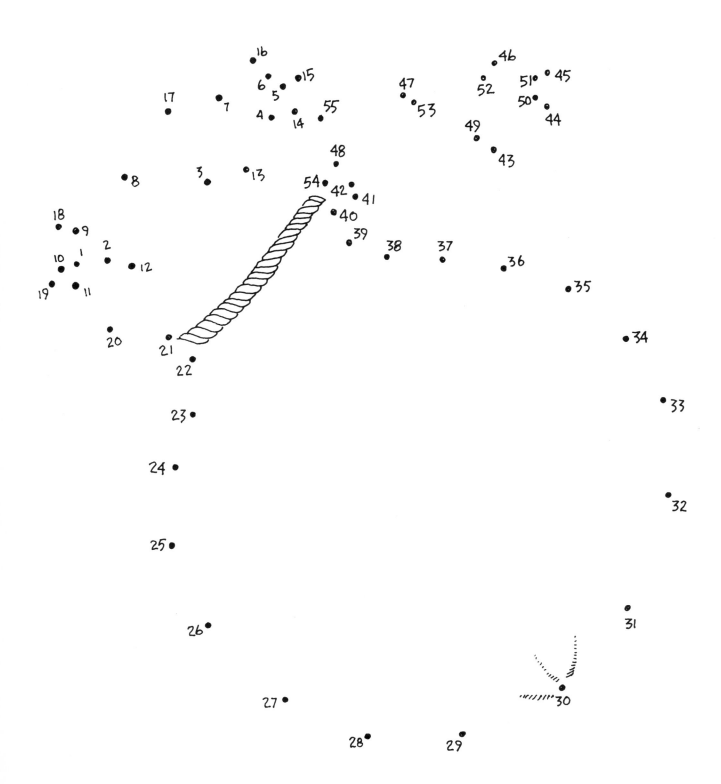

5.

6.

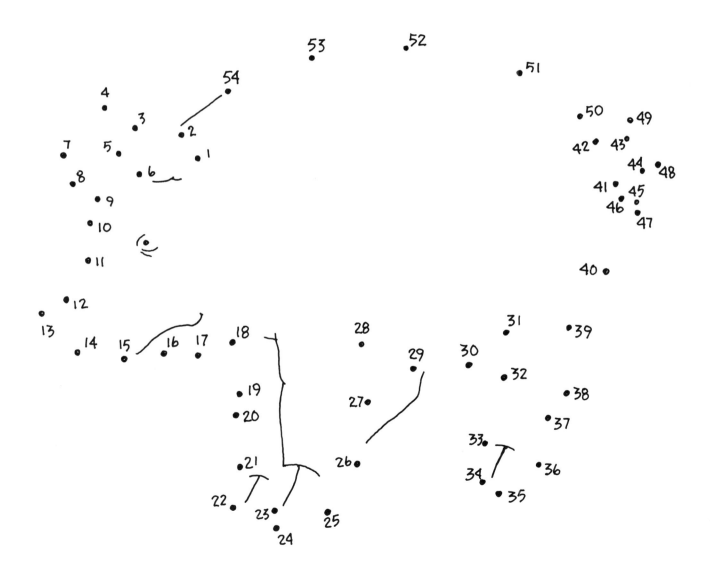

8.

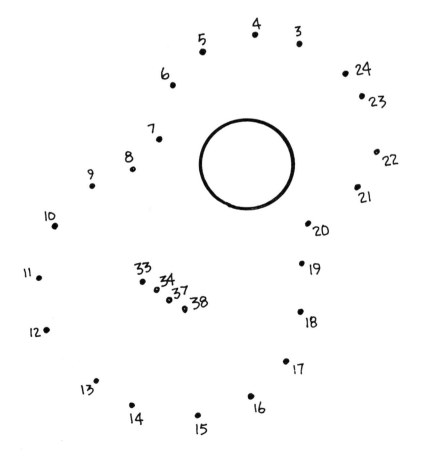

9.

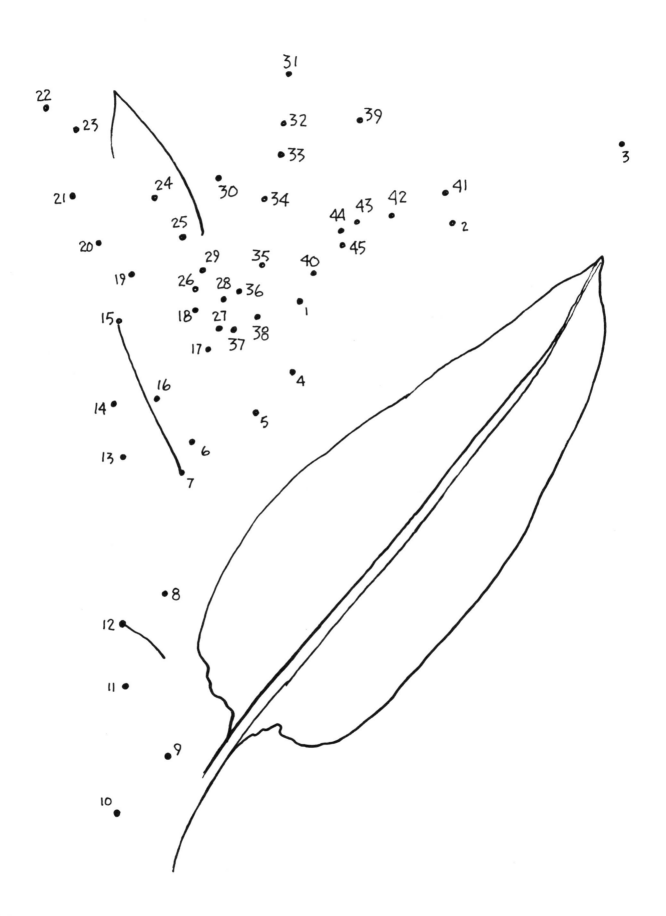

12.

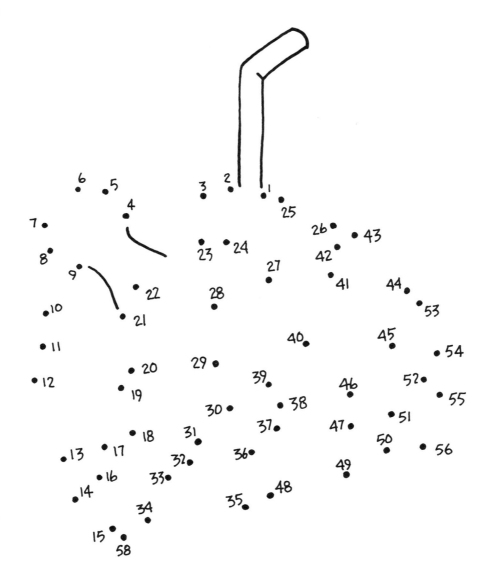

13.

14.

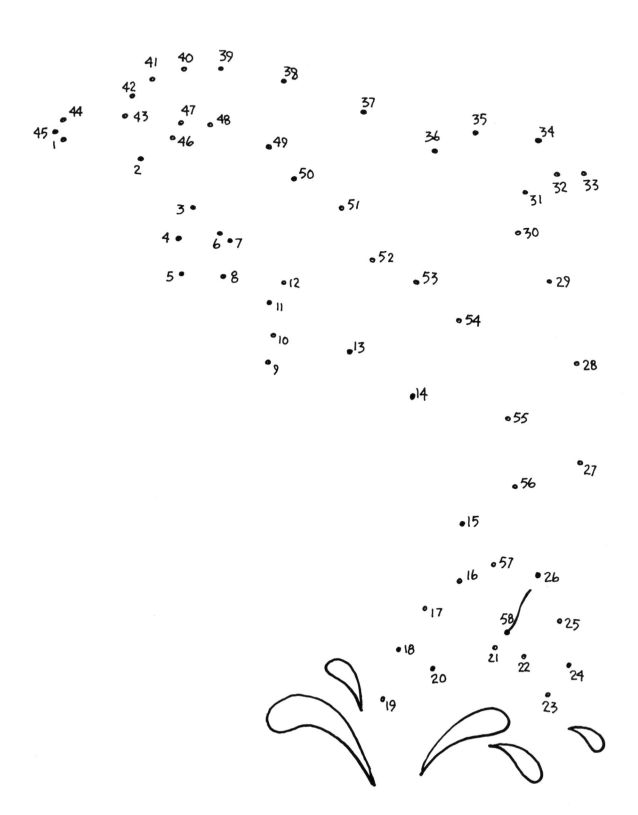

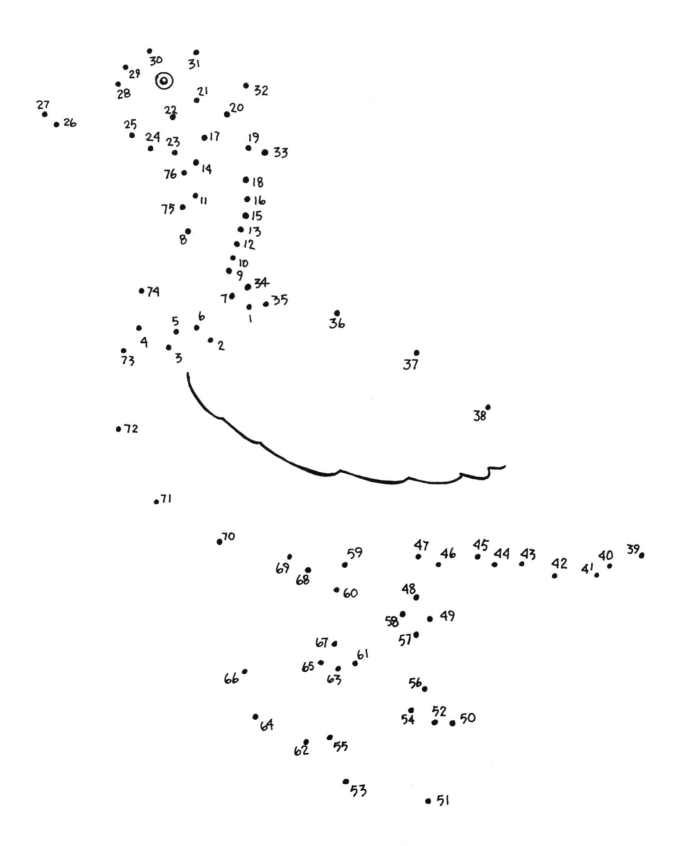

16.

46 44 42
48 40 38
50 43 36
52 39
45 41 31 109
49 47
53 1 51 35 34 108
54 3
2 5 107
4 7 33
55
6 14 31
15 13 32 30
8 106
56 12 29
9
11 10
17 28 105
22 23
57 21 24 27
18 25 26 104
58 19 20
59 60 97 103
64 65 69 74 82 87 91 92 96 102
68 73 81 88
70 80 101
75 86 98
93
63
79
61 78 84 89
66 94 95 99 100
62 67 71 72 76 77 83 85 90

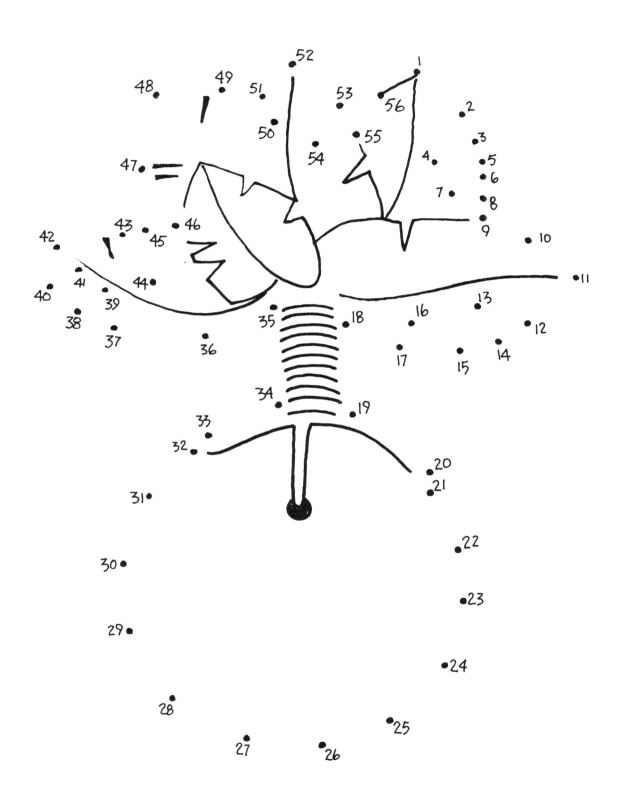

18.

19

20.

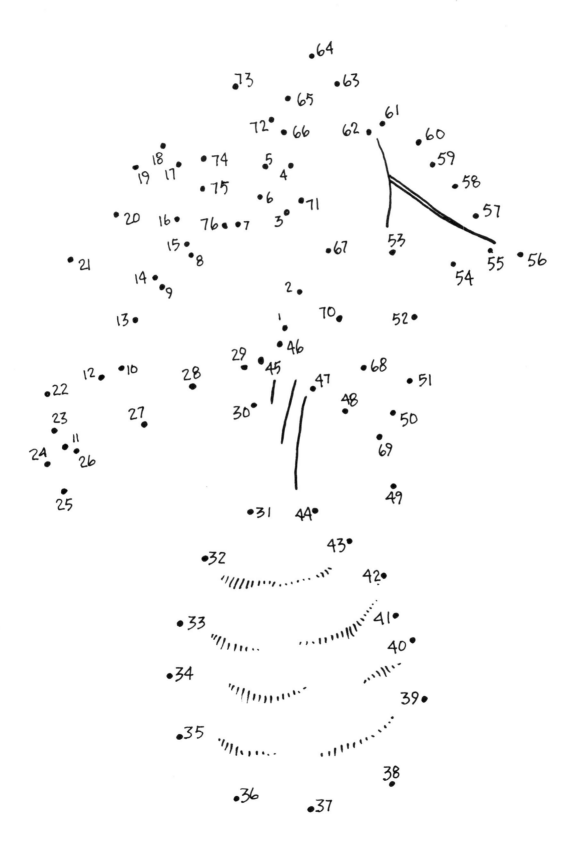

22.

88 87 86 85 84 83 89 90 91 92 93 82 29 28 94 36 30 35 31 27 21 38 34 26 22 20 39 32 37 33 25 23 81 42 40 9 24 43 11 10 19 41 8 44 12 3 2 77 4 1 7 18 47 48 5 6 76 78 80 46 13 17 79 45 50 49 14 66 75 72 51 56 57 15 16 74 73 58 65 67 71 55 59 70 52 54 64 68 69 60 63 53 61 62

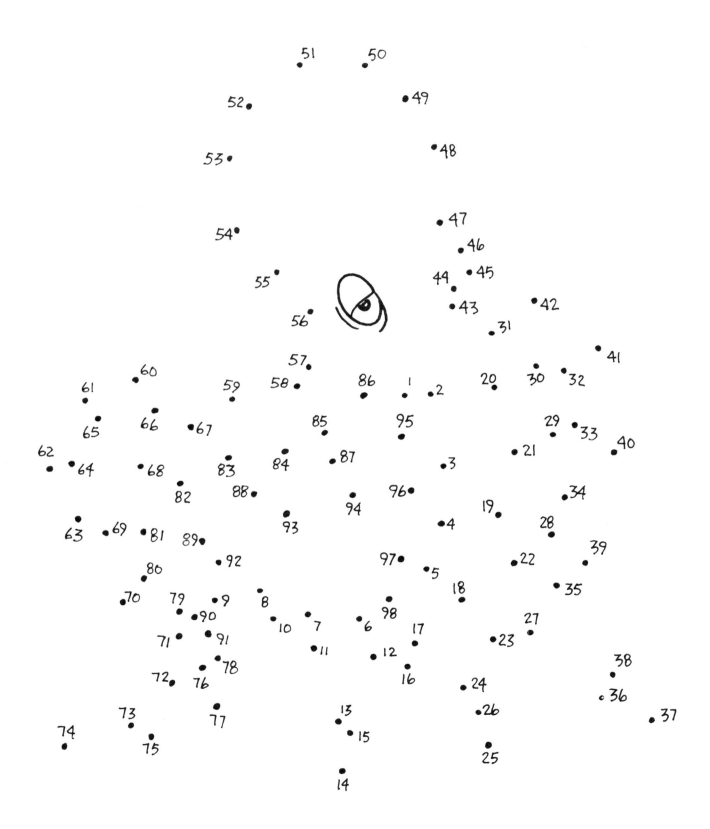

24.

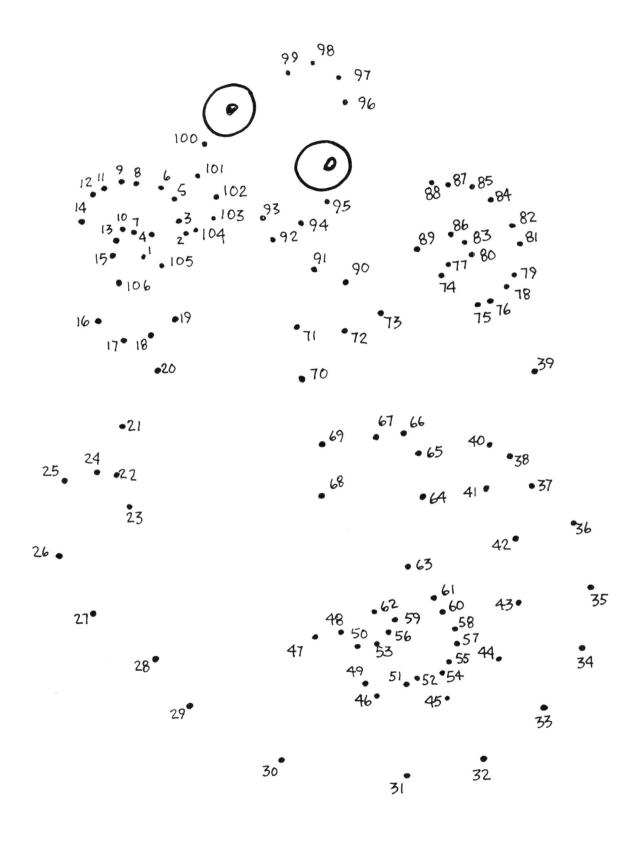

26.

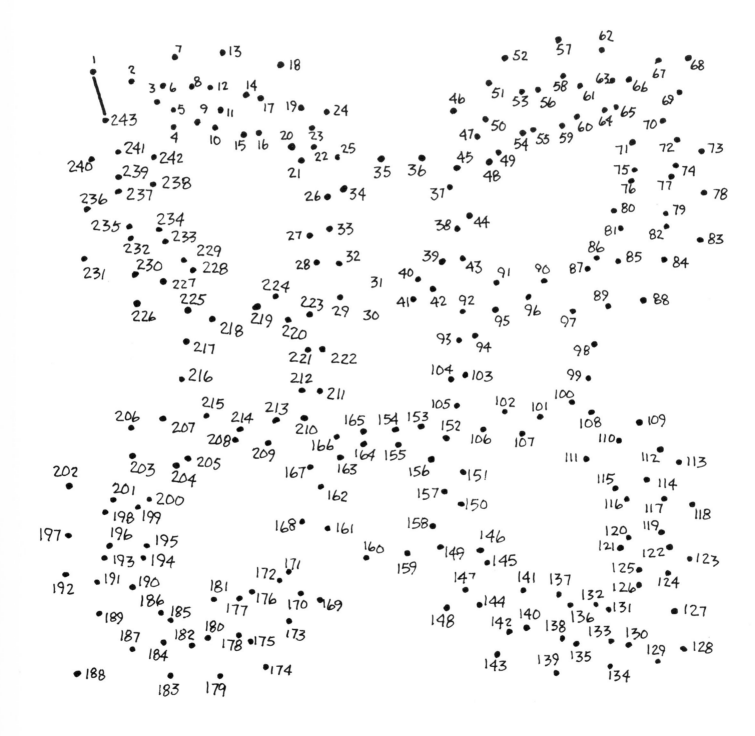

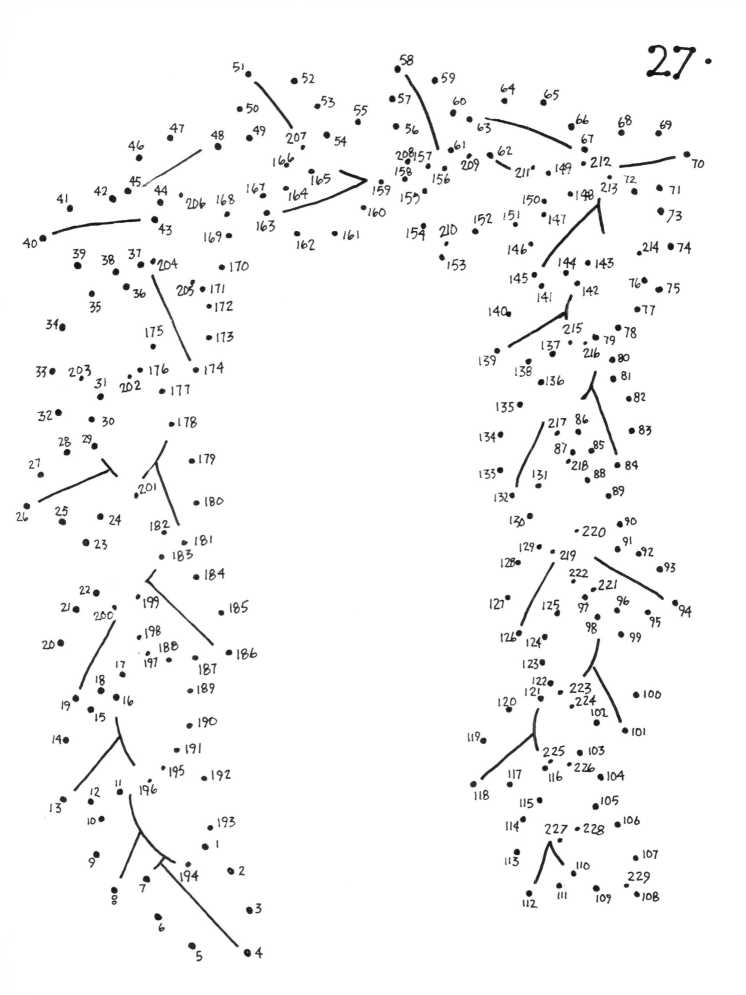

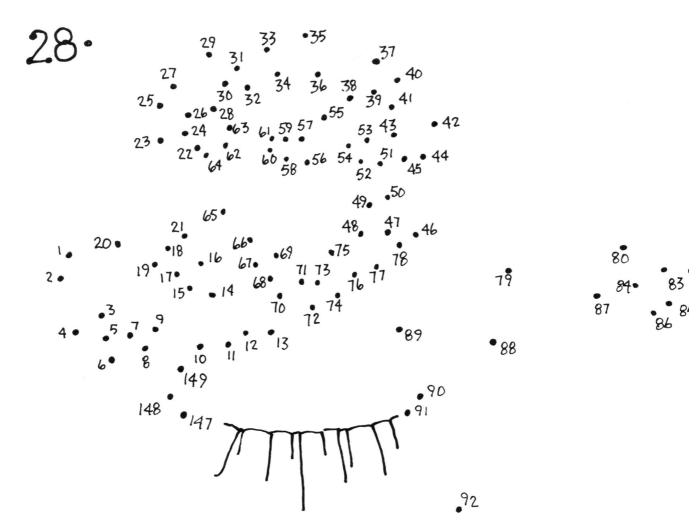

28.

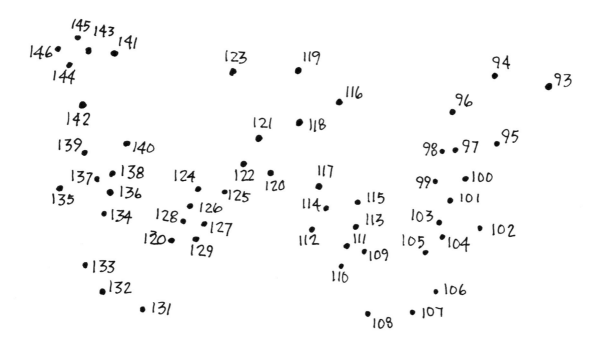

30.

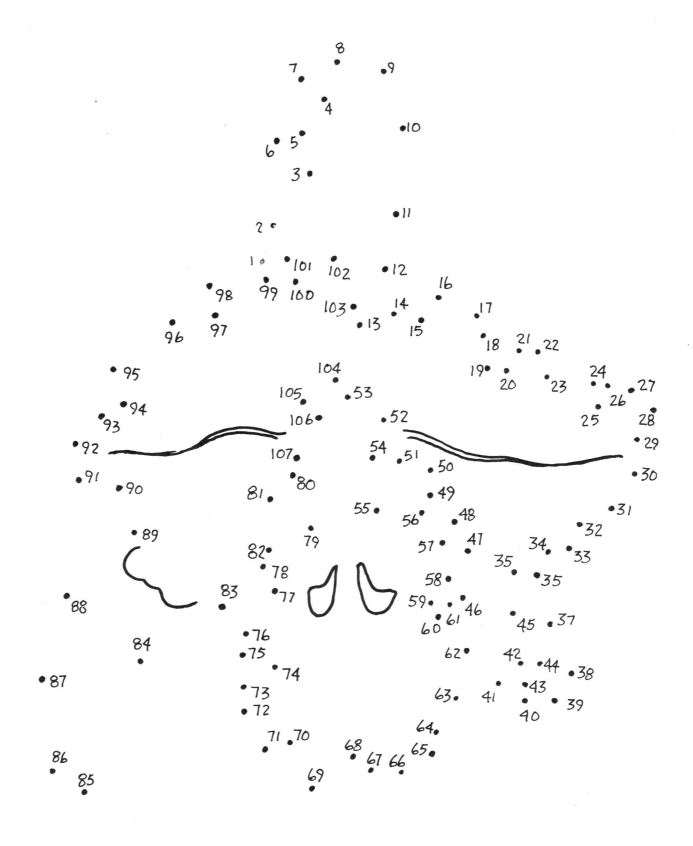